KU-545-392

QUICK START
PIRATES

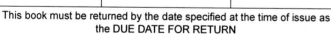

...undie

SCRIBBLERS
a SALARIYA *imprint*

Artist

Isobel Lundie studied illustration and animation at Kingston University in 2015.
She has a special interest in interactive books for children.

How to use this book

Follow the easy, numbered instructions. Simple step-by-step stages enable budding young artists to create their own lively works of art.

What you will need

On each page you will find a list of basic art materials. Some crafts involve the use of scissors, so adult supervision is advised.

Published in Great Britain in MMXVIII by Scribblers, an imprint of
The Salariya Book Company Ltd
25 Marlborough Place,
Brighton BN1 1UB
www.salariya.com

SALARIYA
SCRIBO BOOK HOUSE SCRIBBLERS

© The Salariya Book Company Ltd
MMXVIII

ISBN-13: 978-1-912006-15-1

1 3 5 7 9 8 6 4 2

A CIP catalogue record for this book is available from the British Library.

Printed and bound in Malaysia.

Visit
www.salariya.com
for our online catalogue and **free** fun stuff.

Contents

Crayon Crew

It is much simpler to draw pirates shape by shape! This technique uses pencil crayons to create rich colours by colouring, patterning and scribbling.

You will need:
- Pencil crayons
- Drawing paper

1 Use a black pencil crayon to draw a circle for your pirate's head.

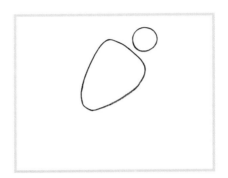

2 Below the circle, draw a curved triangle shape for the pirate's body.

3 Next, draw two curved bean shapes for your pirate's arms.

4 Now add slightly longer bean shapes for your pirate's legs.

5 Draw in the hands and feet, and join the head to the body.

6 Finally, draw in the smaller details, like the face, bandana, vest and boots.

Draw in the background.
You could even draw in
a desert island!

Use a blue pencil to colour
in the pirate's trousers,
then add black to the back
leg to make it darker.

Erase any lines you don't
need, then use pencil
crayons to colour in the
rest of your pirate and
the background.

5

Inky Shark

Ink can be very messy! Make sure you use a palette when you are mixing your inks and always make sure you wash your brushes before changing colours.

You will need:
- Wax crayons
- Thick cartridge paper
- Watercolour paints or inks

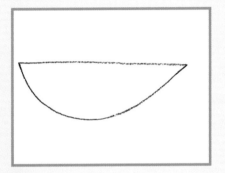

1 Use a blue crayon to draw a semicircle for the shark's body.

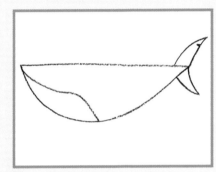

2 Next, draw in the shark's tail fin and tummy.

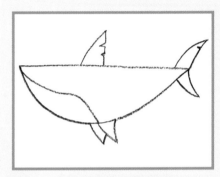

3 Add two fins to the tummy and one torn fin on the shark's back.

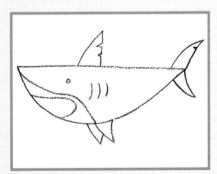

4 Draw the eyes, gills and gaping mouth.

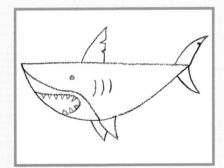

5 Use a pink wax crayon to draw in a row of sharp, jagged teeth.

6 Use blue and pink colours to paint your shark.

Draw in the waves, sea,
seabed and seaweed using
coloured wax crayons.
Add small fish. Now paint
in the background using
watercolour paints.

Use red ink for the
shark's mouth!

7

Tissue Paper Parrot

You will need:
- Felt-tip marker
- Drawing paper
- Tissue paper
  (blue, red and green)
- PVA glue

This project works best if you tear the tissue paper with your hands instead of cutting it with scissors.

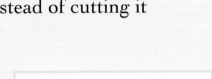

1 Use a black felt-tip to draw a big oval.

2 Draw simple shapes for the parrot's wings.

3 Draw the head with a frilly edge, and three feathers.

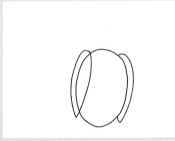

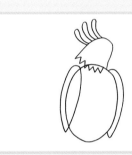

4 Add two legs and a branch for the parrot to perch on.

5 Draw in the tail feathers and the feet.

6 Draw in the parrot's face and beak, and add stripes to the feathers.

Tear your tissue paper into small pieces and glue these onto your drawing.

Tear thin pieces of green tissue paper to make the leaves.

Use two tones of blue on the parrot's wings and try blending them together.

9

Chalk Ship

There are many different ways to use chalks. Try smudging them for smooth colour or scribbbling with them to add texture.

1 Use blue chalk to draw a wavy line for the sea.

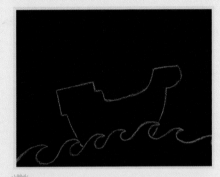

2 Next, use brown chalk to draw the ship's body.

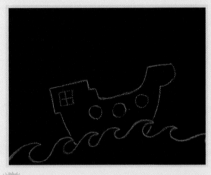

3 Use white chalk to draw in the portholes.

4 Draw in two curved sails with blue chalk.

5 Draw a white skull and crossbones on each sail.

6 Finally, draw in the mast with a flag on top!

Use brown chalk to colour in your ship and draw in its wooden timbers.

Draw in a rough sea with blue and white chalk and then colour it in—why not add a couple of shark fins?

11

Painted Pirate

You will need:
- Poster paints
- Paintbrushes
- White cartridge paper

Always make sure you have different sized brushes before you start. Thin paintbrushes are good for adding small details.

1 Paint a pink circle for the head. Let it dry, then paint in a red bandana.

2 Use red poster paint to paint a curved shape for the body. Add arms.

3 Use blue paint for the pirate's trousers.

4 Now paint her hat, jacket and boots using black paint.

5 Paint white stripes on her T-shirt and spots on her bandana.

6 Add finishing details: her hand, hook, hair, patch, eye, nose, and mouth.

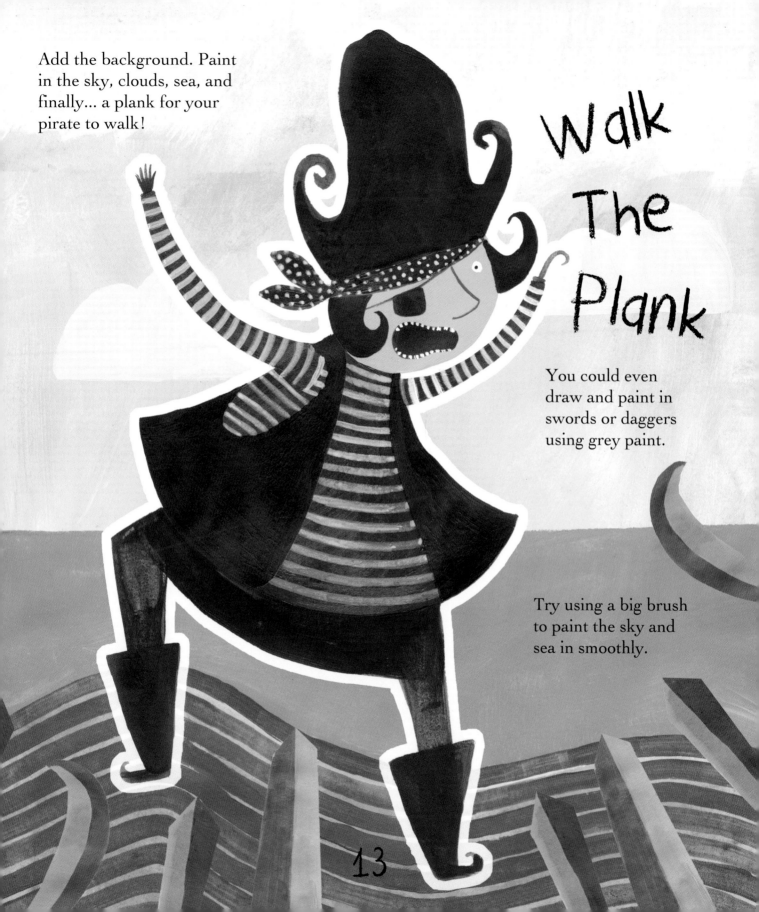

Add the background. Paint in the sky, clouds, sea, and finally... a plank for your pirate to walk!

Walk The Plank

You could even draw and paint in swords or daggers using grey paint.

Try using a big brush to paint the sky and sea in smoothly.

13

Handprint Monkey

Have great fun creating messy handprints,
then draw onto your prints to make a monkey!

You will need:

- Poster paints
- Large paintbrush
- Coloured paper
- Felt-tip pens
- Scissors
- PVA glue

1 Paint your hand with poster paint and press it down onto your paper.

2 Paint a circle for the head and add a long curly tail.

3 Use blue paint for the ears, hands and feet, and face shape.

4 Use a black felt-tip pen to draw in the monkey's face and ears.

5 Add small line marks all over the monkey's body for his fur.

6 Use scissors to cut around your monkey, then glue him onto coloured paper.

Make some fingerprint leaves for the monkeys to eat.

How many handprint monkeys can you make?

Below are some other handprint monkey ideas for you to print and paint.

Stanley

Cheeky

15

Paper cup Pirates

When painting your pirates, try to use the whole width of the brush as you paint. This makes it easier and quicker to cover large areas.

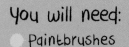

1 Mix three separate colours to paint stripes around your paper cup.

2 Using a smaller brush, paint on the arms, beard, vest and face.

3 Use an even smaller brush to paint the eyes, mouth and scar on his cheek!

4 Draw around the base of the paper cup. Then draw a larger oval around it to make an oval ring shape.

5 Ask an adult to cut out the oval shape. Now paint both sides black.

6 Slide the ring over the pirate's head. Bend the oval up on both sides to make his hat.

It's a good idea to hold the ears in place while the glue dries so they don't fall off!

These mice are different colours. Try out your own ideas – big ears, small ears, or perhaps even draw in a woolly scarf?

Why not draw some leaves or cheese for your mouse to eat – use wax crayons.

17

Cat Pebble

Try to collect the flattest, smoothest pebbles you can as these will be easiest to paint on. Bigger pebbles will also be easier to paint!

You will need:
- Coloured pencil
- Pebbles
- Poster paints
- Paintbrushes
- White paper

1 Choose a small oval pebble and a large squarish one. Paint both white.

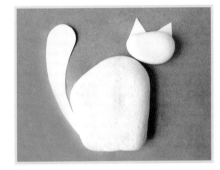

2 Cut paper triangles for the ears and cut a long tail shape. Stick onto the pebble.

3 Pencil in the cat's face, legs, tummy and stripes.

4 Paint the cat's stripes using grey poster paint and a small brush.

5 Add small touches of pink poster paint to the ears and nose.

6 Paint in the remaining details like the eyes, paws and mouth.

Each cat will look different depending on the shape and size of the pebble used. Try out different shapes!

19

Folded Paper Fish

You will need:
- Poster paints
- Paintbrushes
- Square of white paper
- Black felt-tip pen
- Pencil

Make sure you use paper that is thin enough to fold easily.

1 Paint one side of the paper blue. Leave to dry. Fold in half and crease.

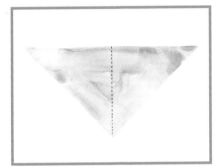

2 Unfold your paper. Now fold and crease the other diagonal.

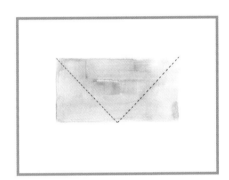

3 Unfold it. Now fold and crease into a rectangle (as shown). Unfold again.

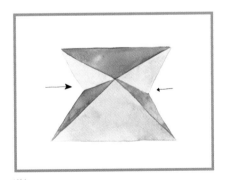

4 Now, push the side folds inwards to make a triangle shape.

5 Fold one front flap over to make a fin.

6 Fold the other flap over it to make another fin. Flip over your fish!

When you've finished, why not paint some seaweed for your fish to swim around?

Pencil in your fish design, then use paint to colour it. Use a black felt-tip pen for the finishing touches.

You could even add bright yellow or red stripes.

If you splat watery blue paint onto wet pink paint you will create this nice splotchy effect.

21

Printed Snake

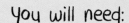
This colourful snake looks great and is fun to make too. Ask an adult to cut your potato!

1 Dip half a potato in red paint, then press onto paper.

2 Use a potato chip shape to print the body.

3 Using a small brush, paint in yellow stripes.

4 Now, paint blue stripes on the snake's body, too.

5 Use a black felt-tip pen to draw in more stripes.

6 Now paint a white circle for the eye and add a black dot. Draw a mouth.

It's a good idea to cut your potato the night before. This gives it time to dry out, which is better for printing.

Halve a potato and paint the flat side purple. Print it three times to make leaves. Once dry, use a black felt-tip pen to add details.

Make sure to give your snake some sharp teeth!

23

Coloured Paper Sausage Dog

You will need:
- Coloured cartridge papers
- PVA glue
- Scissors
- Pencil
- Black felt-tip pen

Choose paper that is thick enough to stand up when folded, but not too thick to cut out small details.

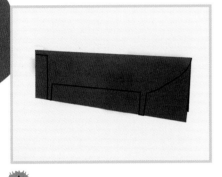

1 Fold an A4 piece of brown cartridge paper in half. Now draw a simple outline of a sausage dog.

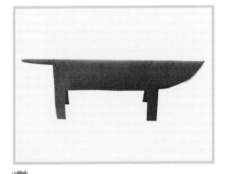

2 Ask an adult to help you carefully cut around the dog-shaped outline.

3 Fold a small piece of dark brown paper in half. Draw a tear shaped ear.

4 Ask an adult to help you cut the shape out. Glue the ears in place.

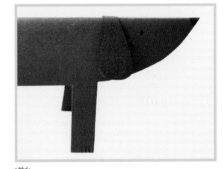

5 Use a black felt-tip pen to add dots for the eyes and to draw the nose and paws.

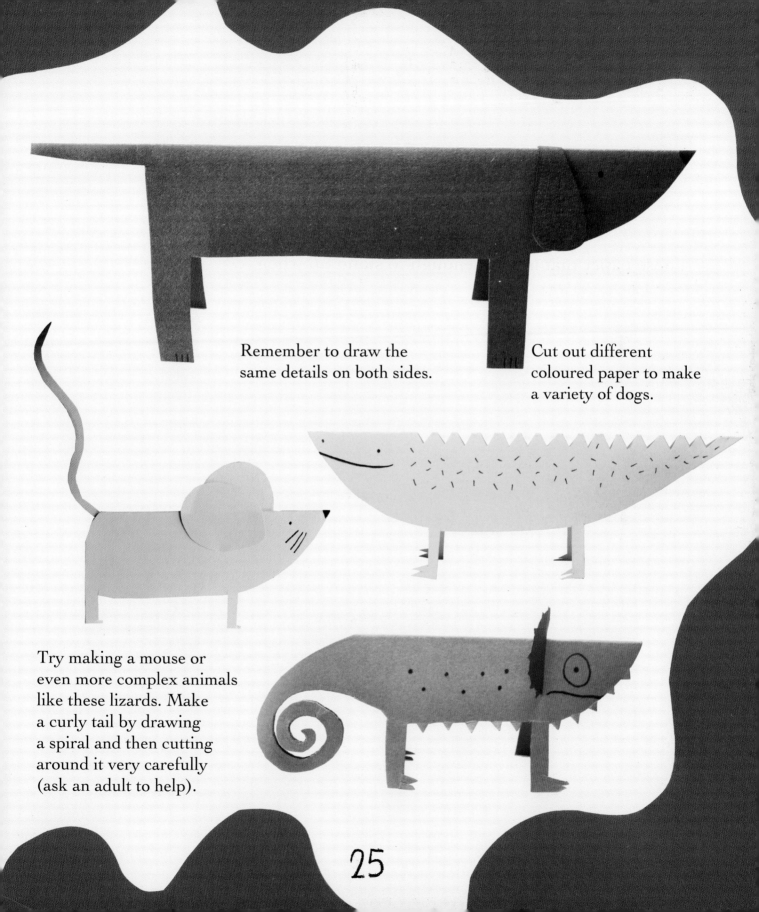

Remember to draw the same details on both sides.

Cut out different coloured paper to make a variety of dogs.

Try making a mouse or even more complex animals like these lizards. Make a curly tail by drawing a spiral and then cutting around it very carefully (ask an adult to help).

Torn Paper Zebra Finch

Make sure that the paper you use is thin enough to rip easily.

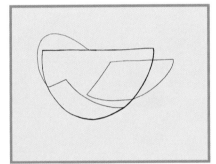

1 Use a pencil to draw a big semicircle on scrap paper.

2 Draw on the bird's wing, head shape and tummy.

3 Draw in its beak and three curved tail feathers.

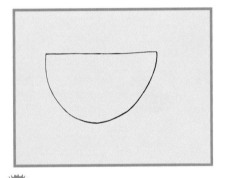

4 Place the outline onto grey coloured paper and create an indent shape of the body by pressing down on the drawing with a pencil.

5 Repeat on different coloured papers for the different body parts. Then tear out the indents.

6 Stick them down in the shape of the bird. Use a black felt-tip and small torn pieces of coloured paper for details.

Try making wings for your zebra finch so it can fly!

Tear some coloured paper to make green leaves and brown branches for the background.

Use leftover paper dots from the hole punch to create perfect round markings!

27

Collage Fish

Make sure you collect a variety of coloured craft papers and magazine cuttings, as these will make the best fish!

You will need:
- Coloured paper
- Newspapers
- Magazines
- Scissors
- PVA glue

1 Cut an oval out of orange paper. Glue onto some plain paper.

2 Cut a fan shaped tail out of grey magazine pages.

3 Cut and stick on four fins using the same paper.

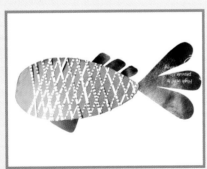

4 Cut long strips of newspaper to stick on in a criss-cross pattern.

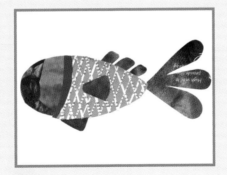

5 Glue on a head shape and a dorsal fin.

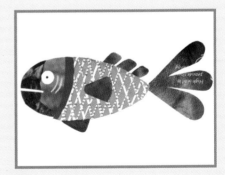

6 Finally, cut out an eye, mouth and gills. Stick onto your fish's head.

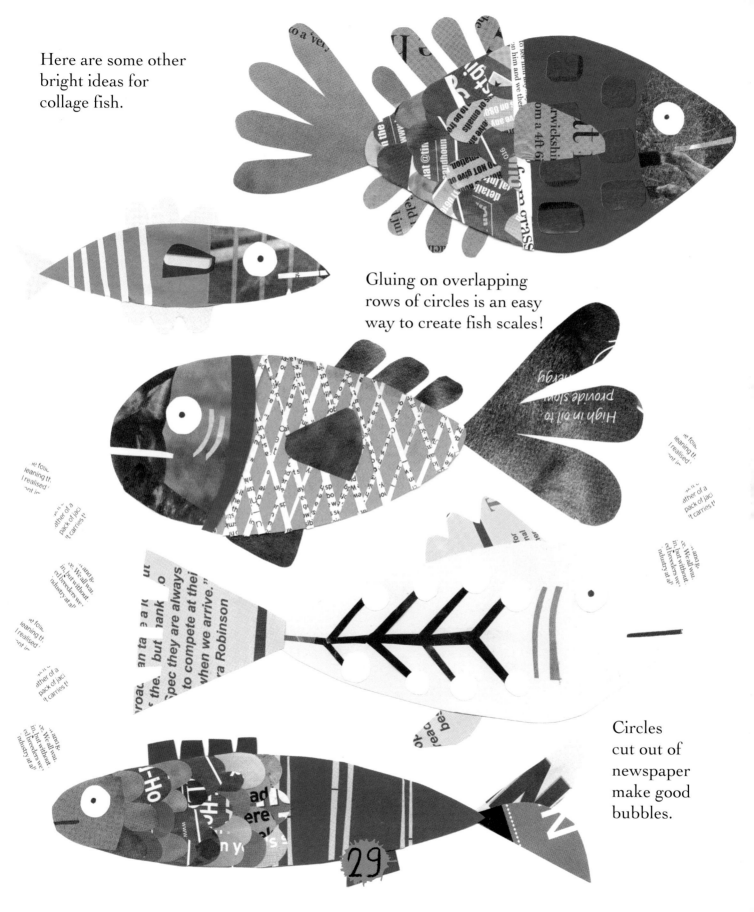

Here are some other bright ideas for collage fish.

Gluing on overlapping rows of circles is an easy way to create fish scales!

Circles cut out of newspaper make good bubbles.

29

Mosaic Chamaeleon

You will need:
- Scissors
- PVA glue
- Coloured papers
- Black paper
- Pencil

Make sure an adult can help you before starting this project as there is a lot of cutting!

1 Use a pencil to draw the head shape and spiral.

2 Draw a big eye and legs. Add another line for the tail.

3 Draw in more details like the mouth and scales.

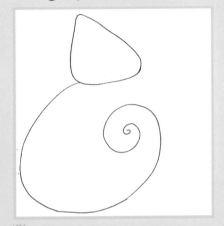

4 Scribble white crayon over the back of your drawing. Place it on black paper. Pencil over the lines to transfer them.

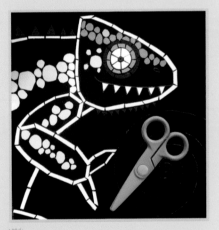

5 Now, using the white crayon guide lines, start to stick down tiles of paper mosaic.

6 Glue on lots of coloured paper mosaics until your chamaeleon is finished!

Alternate body markings by using light and dark green paper to give your chamaeleon stripes!

Use red paper to add spikes along the chamaeleon's spine.

Use long strips of cream paper to outline the chamaeleon's shape.

Glossary

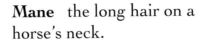

Collage an artwork made from various materials pasted onto a surface.

Dorsal fin the triangular fin found on the backs of many types of fish.

Gills the slits on fishes' necks through which they breathe.

Mane the long hair on a horse's neck.

Mosaic an artwork made from small coloured pieces of glass or other materials.

Palette the container in which an artist mixes different colours of paints.

Texture the look and feel of the surface of a material or picture.

Zebra finch a kind of bird commonly found in Central Australia.

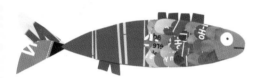

Index